THE CALICOLOUR CAT

Curtis Ackie & Sydney Jackson

For Miko and Yari, of course! - C.A.

To my parents for believing in me and my cat Onion for being cute - S.J.

First published in 2021 by Formy Books
International House
12 Constance Street
London E16 2DQ
formybooks.com

© 2021 Formy Books
Text © 2021 Curtis Ackie
Illustration © 2021 Sydney Jackson

Curtis Ackie has asserted their right to be identified as the author of this work.
Sydney Jackson has asserted their right to be identified as the illustrator of this work.

Designer: Curtis Ackie
Editor: Lauren Ackie

ISBN 978 1 8383 9590 2

1 1 21 21

British Library Cataloguing in Publication Data available.

THE CALICOLOUR CAT

Curtis Ackie

Sydney Jackson

est. 2020
Formy
Books

One warm afternoon
after baking a cake
Miko and Yari feel the table shake.

They reach underneath and
what do they grab?

The **CALICOLOUR CAT**
looking awfully drab!

CALICOLOUR CAT, why are you grey?
What's wrong with you this lovely warm day?

I lost all my feelings in an insolent prank.
The rascally critters left me dry, dull and blank.

Don't worry,
We'll help make you whole.

Come on Yari,
a complete CALICOLOUR CAT is the goal!

We'll search low and high,
we'll search high and low.

Our friend needs our help
so hurry, let's go!

Look there, what is that
behind the TV?

I am **ANGER**, hot rage,
allyuh cyah ketch me!

Oh yes we can,
we are fast, we are quick
and we're putting an end to this
ridiculous trick!

The **CALICOLOUR CAT** is
our friend and
without you they're sick!

Yari, what's that underneath Dad's bedspread?

I am **SADNESS**, alas!
The sorrow, the dread!

Come **SADNESS**, don't be mardy,
get up out of bed!
We're putting an end to your sillyful trick,
the **CALICOLOUR CAT** is our friend
and without you they're sick!

CALICOLOUR CAT, see what we've got!
We searched and we found
and look what we caught!

Now you're no longer dull,
you're grey, red and blue.

But there's much more to do
to make you brand new.

Who could that be
over by the oven glove?

I am deep, I am wide,
I am strong, I am **LOVE**.

Hey **LOVE**, shift yourself,
it's time that we go.
We're putting an end to your
ludicrous trick!
The **CALICOLOUR CAT** is our friend
and without you they're sick.

Look there, in the bush
I see another critter!

I am **FEAR**, don't come near,
you give me the jitters.

No-can-do **FEAR**, get up off your rear!
We're putting an end to your
ridonculous trick!
The **CALICOLOUR CAT** is our friend
and without you they're sick.

CALICOLOUR CAT, see what we've got!
We searched and we found
and look what we caught!

Now you're no longer drab,
no longer not you.

But there's more we must grab
to make you brand new.

Over there, who is that in front of the mirror?

DISGUST, ewww, gross, yuck! Don't come any nearer!

Hey prim-prim **DISGUST**,
you're coming with us!
We're putting an end to your
pappyshow tricks!

The **CALICOLOUR CAT** is our friend
and without you they're sick.

Who do I spy hiding
in the bookshelf?

I am **HAPPINESS**, feeling irie
pull up a seat, come join me!

Sorry **HAPPINESS**, there's no time to lime.
We're putting an end to your
mischievous trick!
The **CALICOLOUR CAT** is our friend
and without you they're sick.

Look what's jumped out of mum's favourite handbag!

Surprise, I'm **SURPRISE**!
Bet you didn't expect me!
I've been waiting,
I knew that you'd come to get me.

Well we're putting an end to your
daft wicked trick!
The **CALICOLOUR CAT** is our friend
and without you they're sick.

CALICOLOUR CAT, see what we've got!
We searched and we found
and look what we caught!

Now you're no longer grey,
no longer not you.

Whoop, whoopie, hooray,
you're all fixed good as new!

Thank you my friends!
My day is no longer bad.
Because of your help
I can be angry or sad.

Because of your eyes
I have disgust and surprise.
Because you were snappy
I am once again happy!

I can holler and cheer
I have love! I have fear!

I can enjoy the weather,
now I'm all back together.

GLOSSARY

allyuh cyah ketch me: you all can't catch me

mardy: sulky, grumpy

prim-prim: overly proper and formal

pappyshow: not serious, clowning around

irie: feeling nice

lime: to hang out

ANGER

SADNESS

LOVE

DISGUST

HAPPINESS

FEAR

SURPRISE